STAR WARS

COLORING & ACTIVITY BOOK

www.starwars.com
© & TM LucasFilm Ltd.

bendon®

The BENDON name, logo and
Tear and Share are trademarks of
Bendon, Ashland, OH 44805.

GALAXY SQUARES

Two players take turns, connecting one icon to another.
Whoever makes the line that completes the box puts their
initials inside that box. The person with the most squares at
the end of the game wins!

STORMTROOPER MATCH

Match the correct helmet to the Stormtrooper.

A

B

C

D

Answer: C

WORD SEARCH

Search the puzzle for the words listed below.

```
U H R Z K M R X A Y
I X Q Y W E A G J P
K S C S D C C Z N F
P K M R V S M I R P
D E O B W J A E J H
A U J X N T T R T A
O Z V Y P H R I R S
V O R A G E F F O M
S M C I T G I L O A
J N F S V I R E P F
V E A R N G S O E A
D L O O T G T G R N
B S T N I Q Y V J V
```

TROOPER   FIRST

ORDER   BLASTER

RIFLE   CAPTAIN

PHASMA   FIGHTER

WORD PATH

Using the letters, in order, from the word FORCE,
follow the correct path to find your way through the maze.

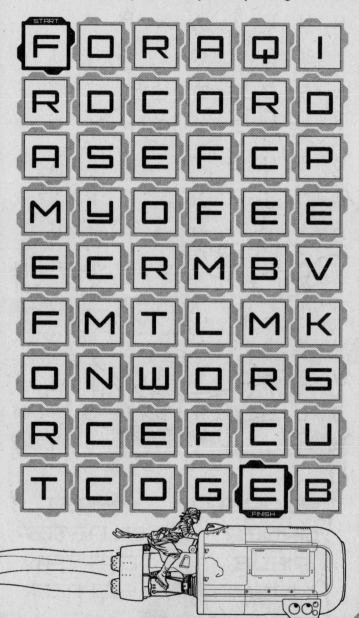

SECTOR GRID

Use the grid to help you complete the picture of Rey.

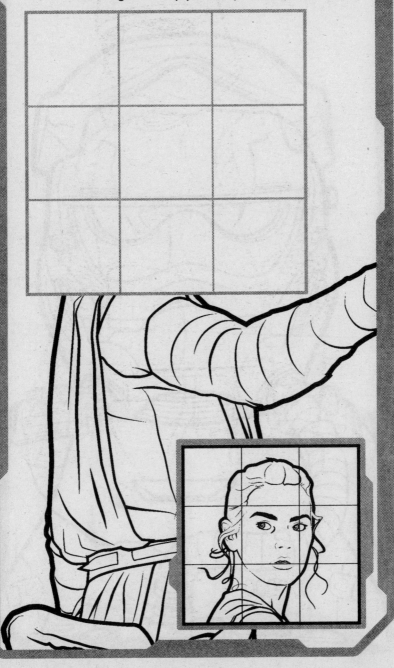

DROID DIFFERENCE

One of these BB units is the one the First Order is seeking.
The one that is different is the real BB-8. Can you find him?

Answer: D

HOW MANY WORDS

How many different words can you make from the letters in
KNIGHTS OF REN?

GALAXY SQUARES

Two players take turns, connecting one icon to another.
Whoever makes the line that completes the box puts their
initials inside that box. The person with the most squares at
the end of the game wins!

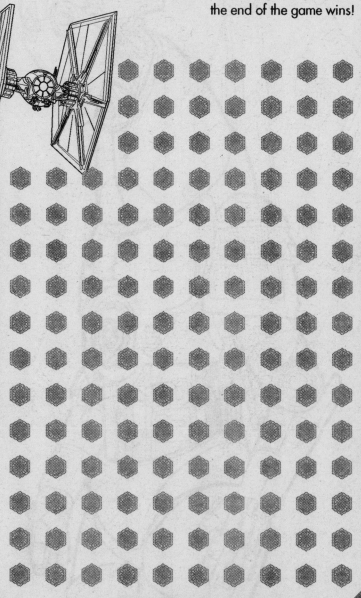

WORD PATH

Using the letters, in order, from the word FALCON,
follow the correct path to find your way through the maze.

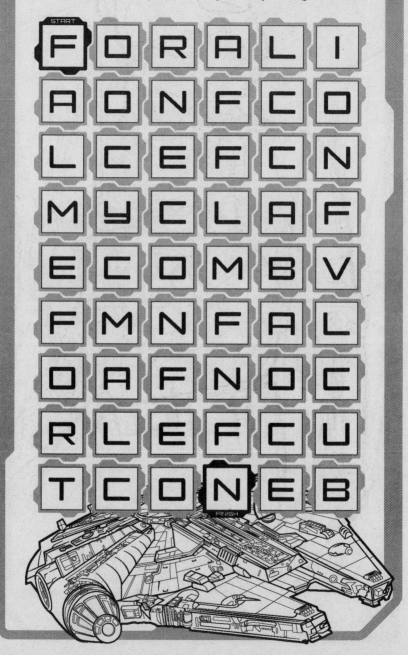

START

F	O	R	A	L	I
A	O	N	F	C	O
L	C	E	F	C	N
M	Y	C	L	A	F
E	C	O	M	B	V
F	M	N	F	A	L
O	A	F	N	O	C
R	L	E	F	C	U
T	C	O	N	E	B

FINISH

© & TM 2016 LucasFilm Ltd.

WORD SEARCH

Search the puzzle for the words listed below.

```
T M D A L E A D E R
I I M A X T G M D P
Q O E I R D D S E K
M S E F J I V N S Y
M S H S I B N O T L
P Z M B W G Q W R O
U A T Y V V H M O R
R Z O Q N T Z T Y E
S U P R E M E K E N
T N N S O T Q Y R R
Q I Y G F Q P B N K
R A P O W E R F H L
I A F L A M E X N M
```

SNOW   SUPREME

FLAME   KYLO REN

TIE FIGHTER   LEADER

DESTROYER   POWER

DESIGN PAGE

Design your own droid.

WORD PATH

Using the letters, in order, from the word LIGHTSIDE,
follow the correct path to find your way through the maze.

START L	O	R	A	I	G
I	D	C	O	L	H
G	S	I	D	E	T
H	T	N	F	I	S
E	C	R	E	D	V
H	G	I	L	M	K
T	N	I	G	H	T
S	E	L	D	I	S
I	D	D	E FINISH	R	B

STARSHIP MATCH

Match the ships to their correct details below.

A ☐ ☐

B ☐ ☐

C ☐ ☐

1

2

3

4

5

6

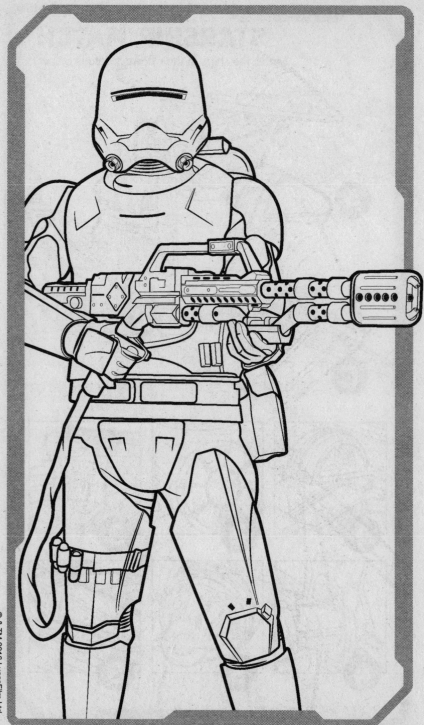

SECTOR GRID

Use the grid to help you complete the picture of Kylo Ren.

WORD SEARCH

Search the puzzle for the words listed below.

```
S S K U G I D D B P
Y Q I T H V X A U D
L Z A T I O H N T A
I T O L H R F H O R
G Z S Q L L G G J K
H J A G M I O V J S
T L B S N A D R X I
F L R K A T S J D D
T F E F H Z X T E E
N O Y Q O V O Q E T
B R S I U C T K O R
B C O X Z R F F E J
J E K Y L O R E N C
```

DARKSIDE

LIGHT

MASTER

KYLO REN

FORCE

SABRE

SITH LORD

KNIGHT

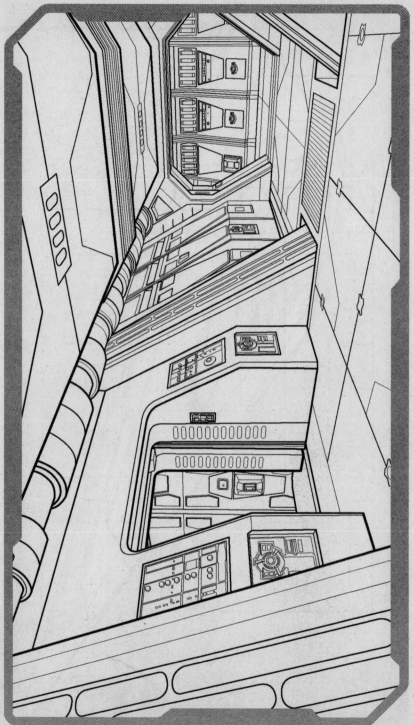

MAZE ESCAPE

Help Rey and Finn through the maze to the Millennium Falcon.

SECTOR GRID

Kylo Ren's shuttle is unique. Find the one that is different.

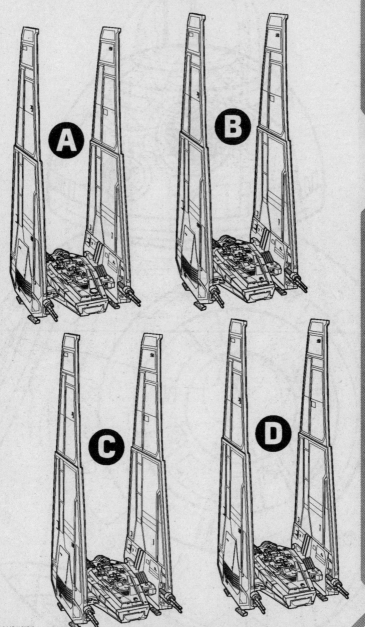

GALAXY SQUARES

Two players take turns, connecting one icon to another.
Whoever makes the line that completes the box puts their
initials inside that box. The person with the most squares at
the end of the game wins!

HOW MANY WORDS

How many different words can you make from the letters in
TIE FIGHTER?

_____

_____

_____

_____

_____

_____

_____   _____

_____   _____

_____   _____

_____   _____

_____   _____

_____   _____

_____   _____

_____   _____

_____   _____

SECTOR GRID

Use the grid to help you complete the picture of C-3PO.

WORD PATH

Using the letters, in order, from the word SITHLORD,
follow the correct path to find your way through the maze.

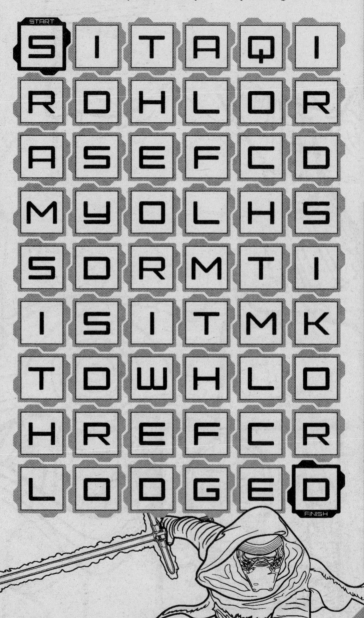

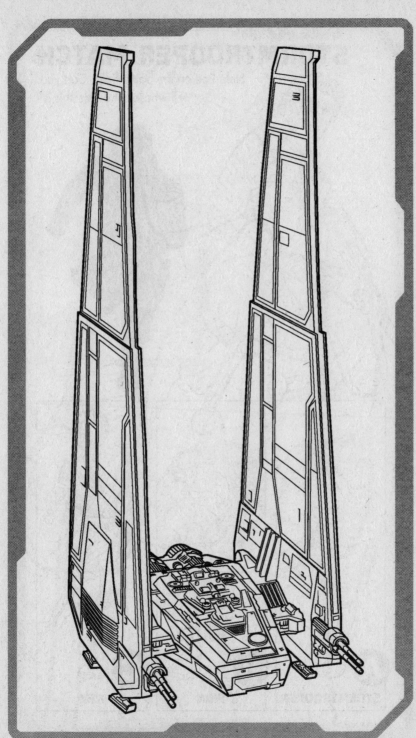

STORMTROOPER MATCH

Help Poe on the battle field. Can you tell whose silhouette this is?

A STORMTROOPER

B FINN

C REY

Answer: A

SQUADRON LEADER

X-Wing squadron leaders like their fighters to stand out.
Can you spot the squadron leader's X-Wing?

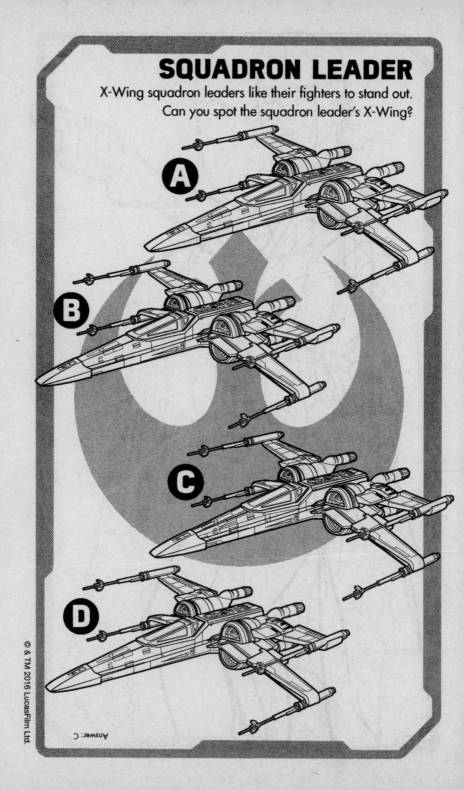

Answer: C

GALAXY SQUARES

Two players take turns, connecting one icon to another. Whoever makes the line that completes the box puts their initials inside that box. The person with the most squares at the end of the game wins!

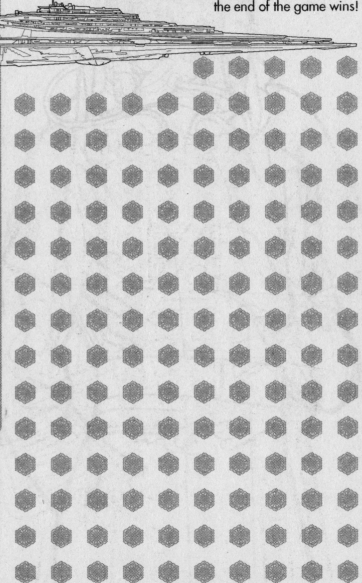

WORD PATH

Using the letters, in order, from the word FIRSTORDER, follow the correct path to find your way through the maze.

WORD SEARCH

Search the puzzle for the words listed below.

```
G P Y P W L N 8 K V
Y O 3 B J Y R I J F
8 E R M B J V 2 C A
E D C 2 H 8 T U R L
Q A H E A F T Y E C
Y M E Z N I W N Y O
O E W S S T C O F N
3 R B I O H 3 N I F
T O A P L C P K N J
C N C P O L O 2 N I
P H C R 2 D 2 A M B
L B A Y Q C O U 8 C
2 8 I N 3 O S H W A
```

REY FINN   CHEWBACCA

HAN SOLO   FALCON

POE DAMERON   R2-D2

C-3PO   BB-8

SECTOR GRID

Use the grid to help you complete the picture of Poe.

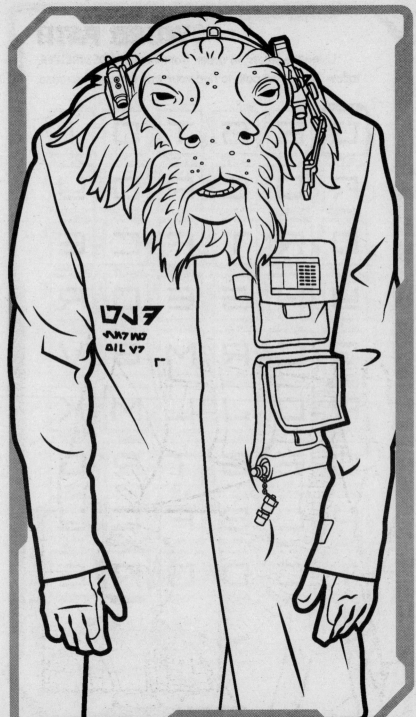

WORD PATH

Using the letters, in order, from the word DESTROYER,
follow the correct path to find your way through the maze.

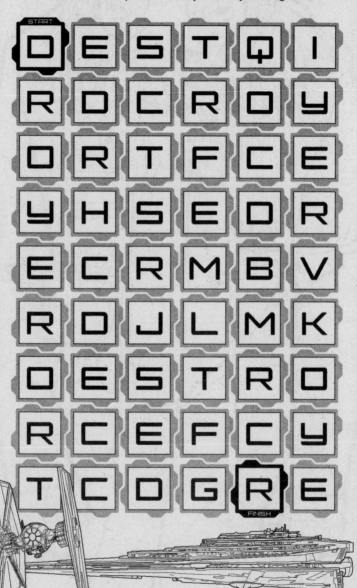

DESIGN PAGE

Draw a Jedi Knight.

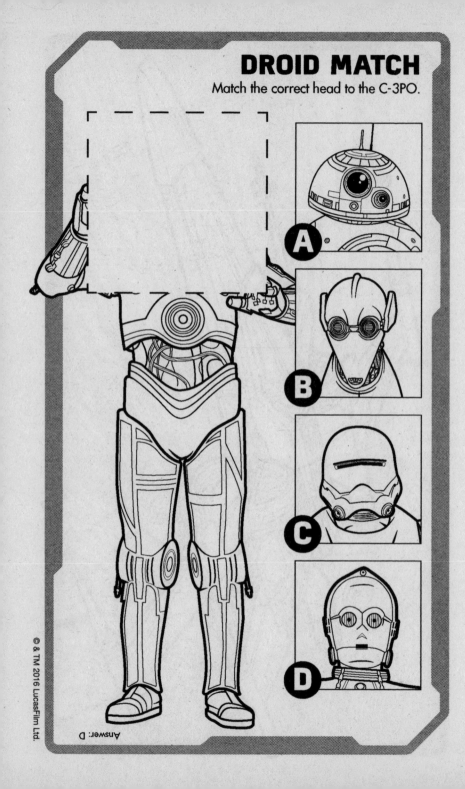

DROID MATCH

Match the correct head to the C-3PO.

A

B

C

D

Answer: D

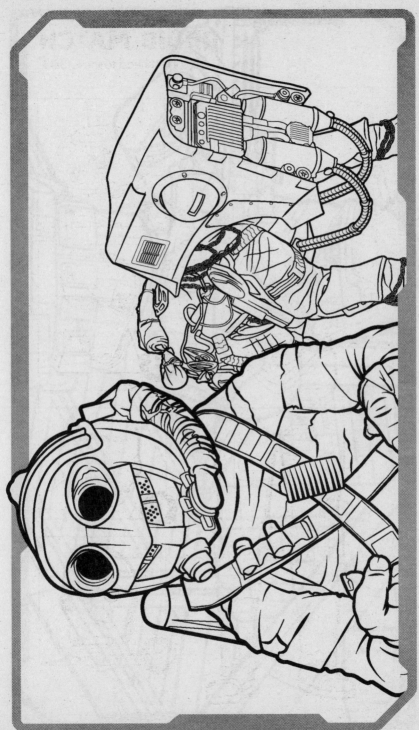

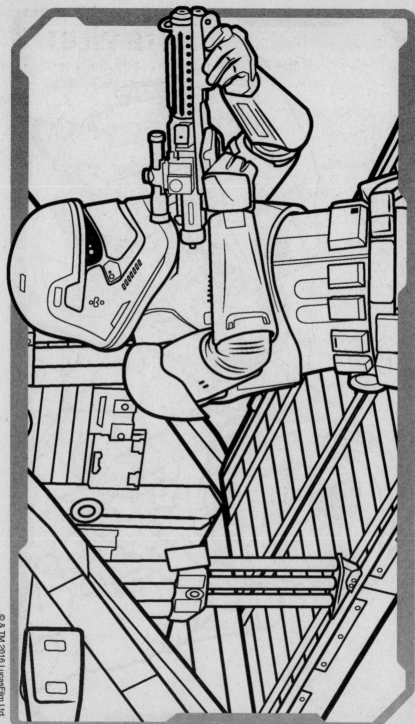

ELITE PILOT

Elite TIE-Fighter pilots wear special markings.
See if you can spot the best pilot.

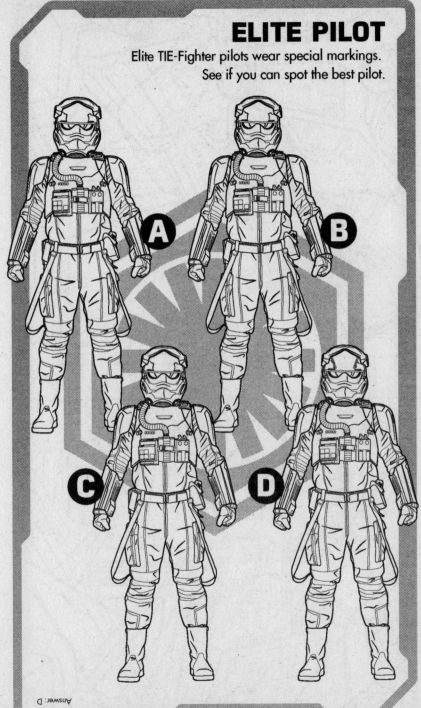

Answer: D

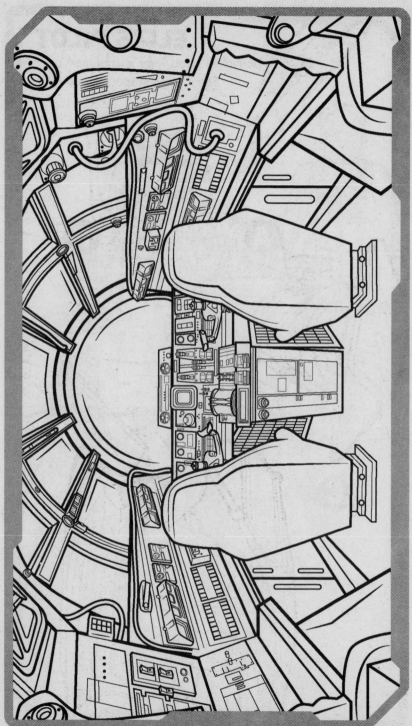

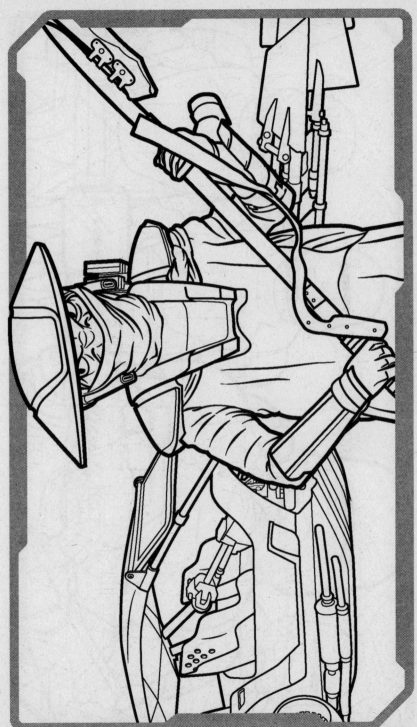

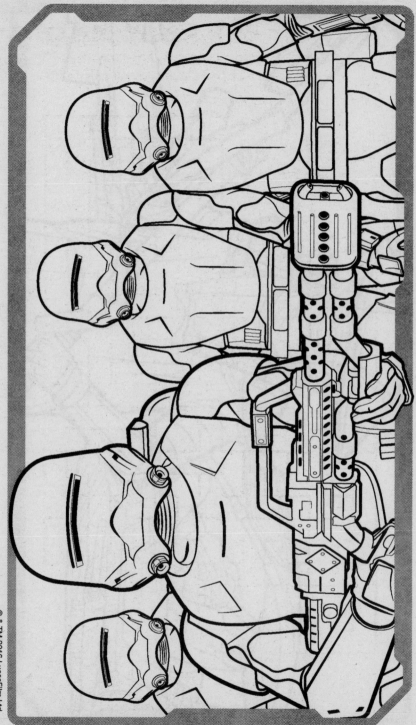

GET AWAY MAZE

Follow the maze to help Poe escape the
First Order in a stolen TIE-Fighter.

WORD SEARCH

Search the puzzle for the words listed below.

```
M  V  S  G  K  W  V  Q  W  R
Y  I  U  T  G  I  O  F  E  T
M  A  L  N  A  M  O  T  H  R
N  S  I  L  T  R  H  G  A  M
C  W  P  L  E  G  A  A  S  H
X  N  D  A  I  N  S  G  C  L
I  G  H  F  C  O  N  E  Z  G
Q  X  E  Q  A  E  M  I  W  V
R  I  U  Y  P  O  U  J  U  I
T  B  Y  U  R  T  Q  Q  Y  M
D  E  S  T  R  O  Y  E  R  K
N  L  S  P  E  E  D  E  R  Y
Y  A  M  K  X  G  G  A  P  E
```

X-WING   TIE FIGHTER
SPEEDER   MILLENNIUM
ASTROMECH   SPACE
STAR   DESTROYER

HOW MANY WORDS

How many different words can you make from the letters in
MILLENNIUM FALCON?

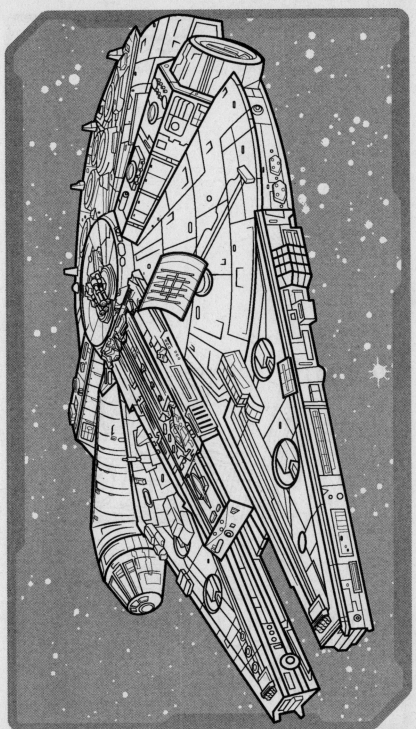

SECTOR GRID

Use the grid to help you complete the picture of R2-D2.

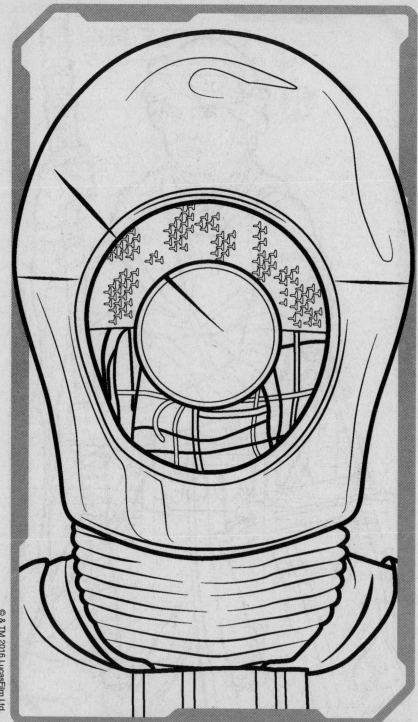

VEHICLE MATCH

Match the vehicles to their correct details below.

A ☐ ☐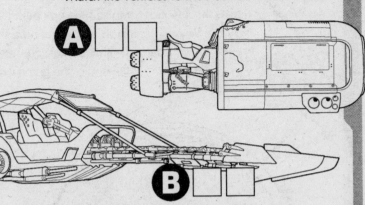

B ☐ ☐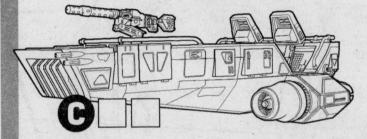

C ☐ ☐

1

2

3

4

5

6

GALAXY SQUARES

Two players take turns, connecting one icon to another. Whoever makes the line that completes the box puts their initials inside that box. The person with the most squares at the end of the game wins!

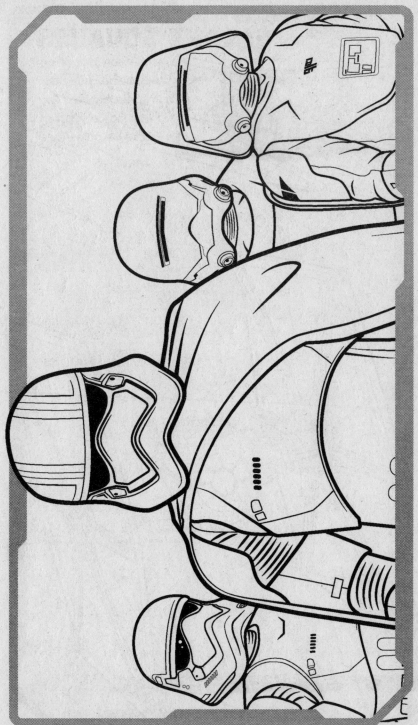

WORD SEARCH

Search the puzzle for the words listed below.

```
R L J J H A J M G X
W E K D X B R L V S
M P S M G T H 3 R 2
V K N I X D R K A V
V L A K S F 2 2 S P
E U S T F T R H D D
E G T R D M A B F 2
R A R E R F Y N Y K
Z B O Y O Y 8 Q C B
B E M F I Y G S N E
B A E I D 3 R W W W
3 S C N K C 3 P O U
A T H N X Y V V Q Y
```

DROID
ASTROMECH
R2-D2
C-3PO

BB-8
REY FINN
RESISTANCE
LUGABEAST

© & TM 2016 LucasFilm Ltd.

DESIGN PAGE

Draw an alien.

WORD PATH

Using the letters, in order, from the word FINNREY,
follow the correct path to find your way through the maze.

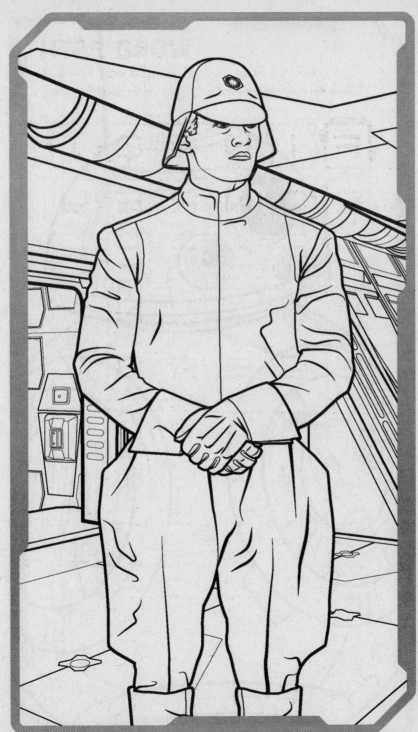

ASTROMECH CHALLENGE

Astromechs are a very useful droid to have around.
But only one of these droids is our loyal R2-D2.
Can you spot the droid that is different

Answer: B

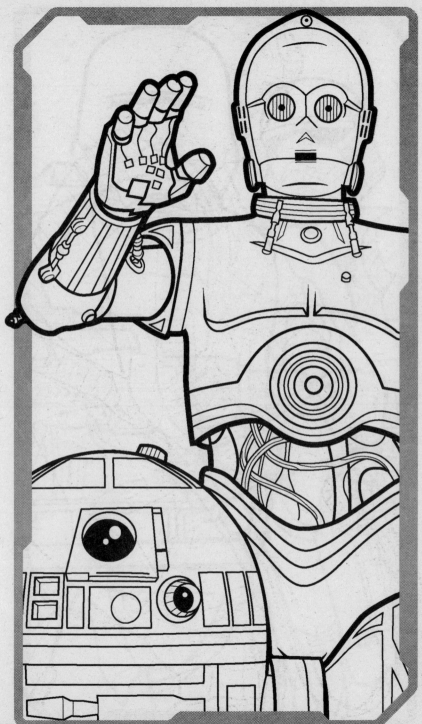

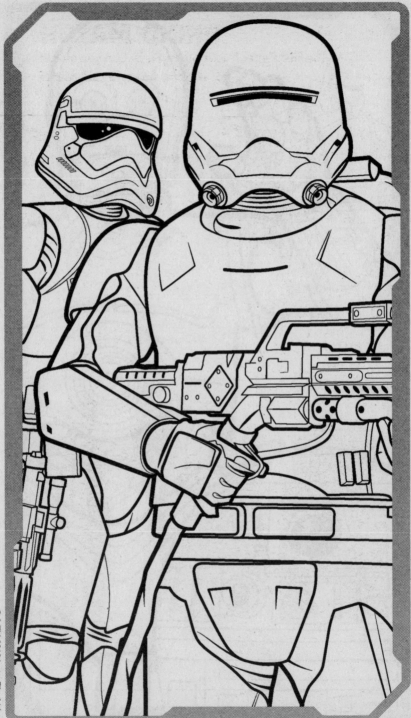

DROID MATCH

The First Order is looking for BB-8. Can you match the droid to the correct silhouette?

BB-8

A

B

C

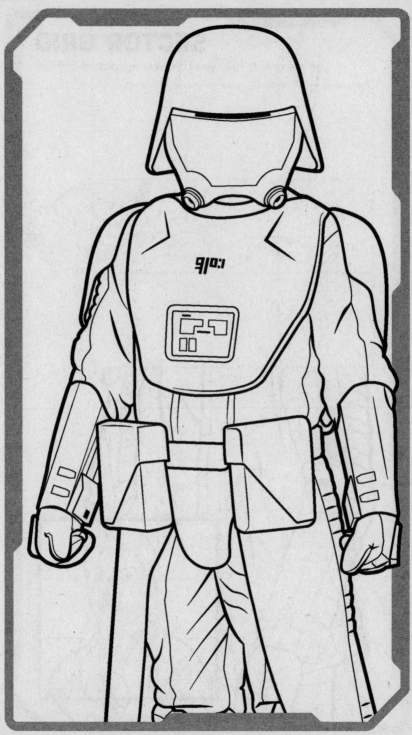

SECTOR GRID

Use the grid to help you complete the picture of Finn.

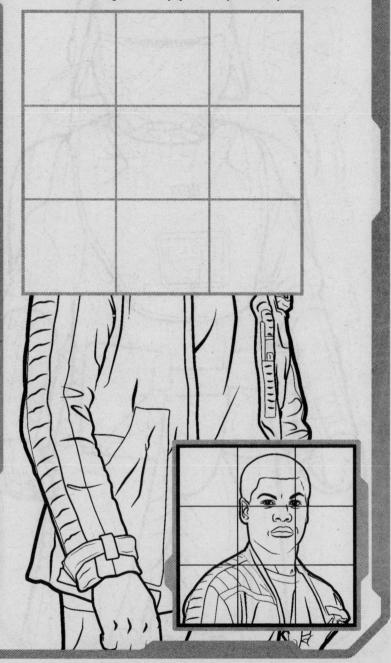

WORD PATH

Using the letters, in order, from the word RESISTANCE,
follow the correct path to find your way through the maze.

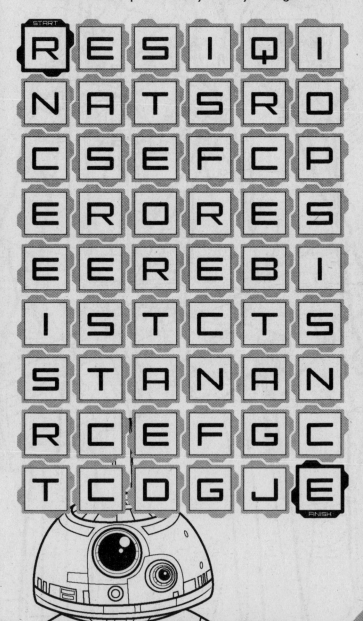

START

R	E	S	I	Q	I
N	A	T	S	R	O
C	S	E	F	C	P
E	R	O	R	E	S
E	E	R	E	B	I
I	S	T	C	T	S
S	T	A	N	A	N
R	C	E	F	G	C
T	C	D	G	J	E

FINISH

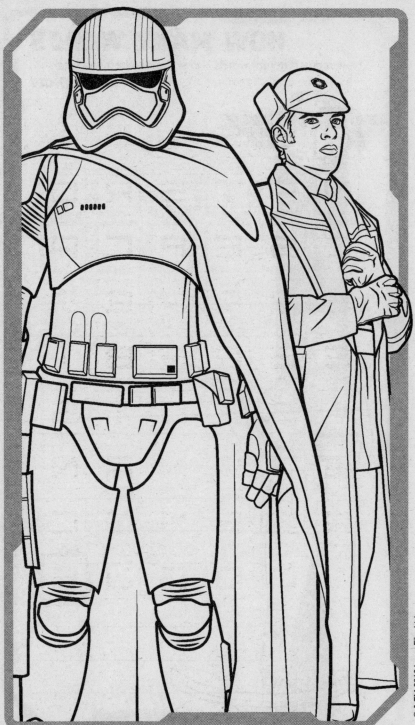

HOW MANY WORDS

How many different words can you make from the letters in
RESISTANCE?

_____

_____

_____

_____

_____

_____

_____

_____

_____

_____

_____

_____

_____

_____

_____

_____

_____

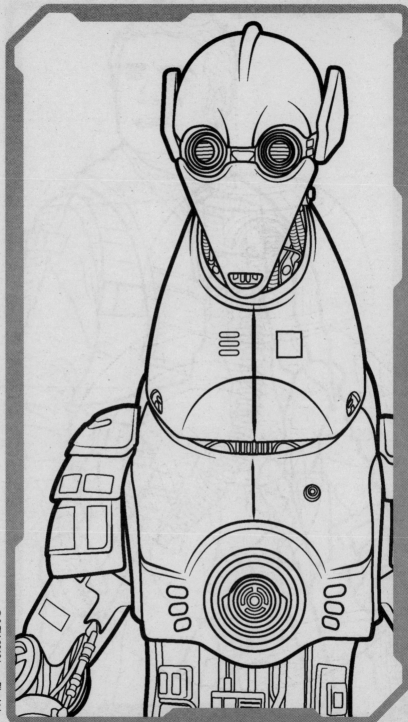

GALAXY SQUARES

Two players take turns, connecting one icon to another.
Whoever makes the line that completes the box puts their
initials inside that box. The person with the most squares at
the end of the game wins!

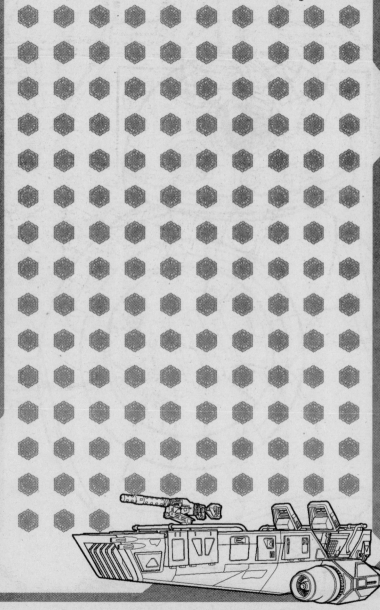

DESERT MAZE

Guide BB-8 through the maze to avoid the
First Order in the desert of Jakku.

MILLENNIUM MIX-UP

Han Solo and Chewbacca have looked all over the galaxy for their lost ship. Can you spot one of the details that makes the Millennium Falcon a one of a kind?

A

B

C

Answer: A

ALIEN MATCH

Match Chewbacca's body with the correct head.

A

B

C

D

Answer: B

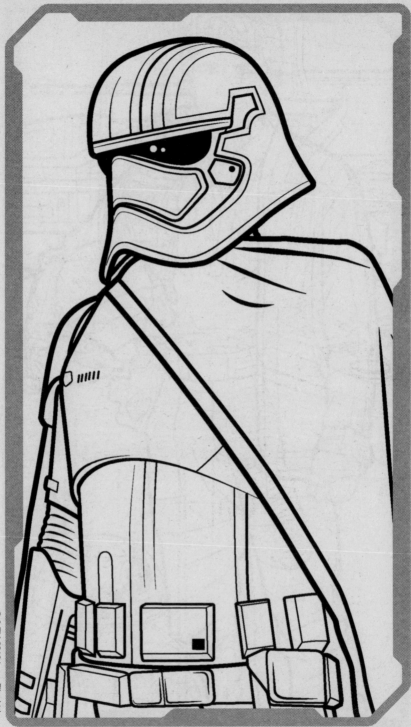

SECTOR GRID

Use the grid to help you complete the picture of a Stormtrooper.

WORD SEARCH

Search the puzzle for the words listed below.

```
Q M O A R W I Z X X
F J X C S U W R U W
V E A C T N E T J I
Z D C Q A D I I I N
G I O N R N J E Y G
M N N O W O V F F E
C N L E A E S I H P
F U H X R D I G S B
I F F X S N T H F F
R E B E L S H T E G
S V T P E C W E S F
T N O R P K A R T W
V K J C T O R K G X
```

STAW WARS   **JEDI**
SITH   **TIE FIGHTER**
X-WING   **REBELS**
FIRST   **ORDER**

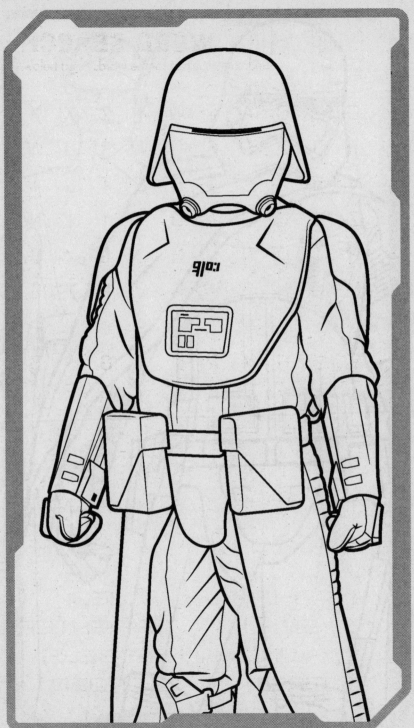

GALAXY SQUARES

Two players take turns, connecting one icon to another. Whoever makes the line that completes the box puts their initials inside that box. The person with the most squares at the end of the game wins!

DESIGN PAGE

Design your own space ship.

TROOPER TRAINING

A Trooper of the First Order must have an attention for details.
Can you spot 5 differences between theses images
of Captain Phasma?

Answers: 1. Lines on helmet, 2. Dots on chest, 3. Square on belt, 4. Back of glove, 5. Line on leg.

HOW MANY WORDS

How many different words can you make from the letters in
CAPTAIN PHASMA?

_____

_____

_____

_____

_____

_____

_____

_____

_____

_____

_____

_____

_____

_____

_____

_____

_____

_____

WORD SEARCH

Search the puzzle for the words listed below.

```
S  A  B  R  E  W  D  P  Y  O
R  T  D  C  Z  V  G  G  Y  T
I  H  E  B  R  J  G  P  D  G
B  E  T  J  T  L  K  O  P  P
L  R  O  F  A  Z  L  Y  Z  V
A  M  N  O  B  F  I  S  K  N
S  A  A  R  U  R  G  W  K  Z
T  L  T  C  P  I  H  U  B  E
E  L  O  E  Y  T  T  X  L  F
R  T  R  C  H  Z  N  F  F  W
T  O  B  G  L  S  I  X  L  I
E  O  I  S  W  R  N  X  I  C
W  L  Z  E  Z  I  G  C  M  G
```

BLASTER **THERMAL**
RIFLE **DETONATOR**
LIGHT **FORCE**
SABRE **LIGHTNING**

VEHICLE MATCH

Match the vehicles to their correct details below.

A ☐ ☐

B ☐ ☐

C ☐ ☐

1 **2** **3**

4 **5** **6**

Answer: A-1 & 5, B-2 & 4, C-3 & 6

SECTOR GRID

Use the grid to help you complete the picture of BB-8.

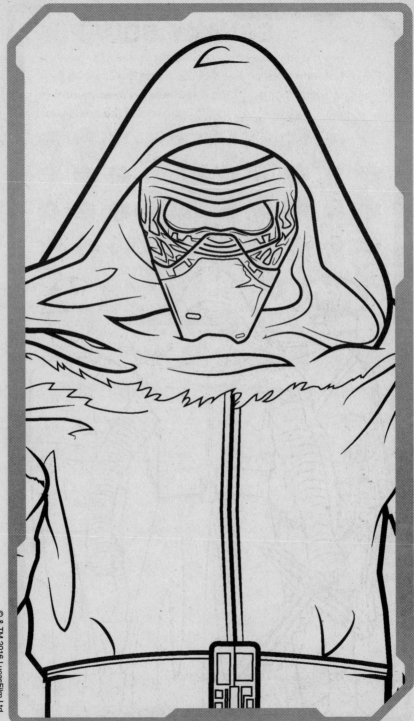

GALAXY SQUARES

Two players take turns, connecting one icon to another. Whoever makes the line that completes the box puts their initials inside that box. The person with the most squares at the end of the game wins!

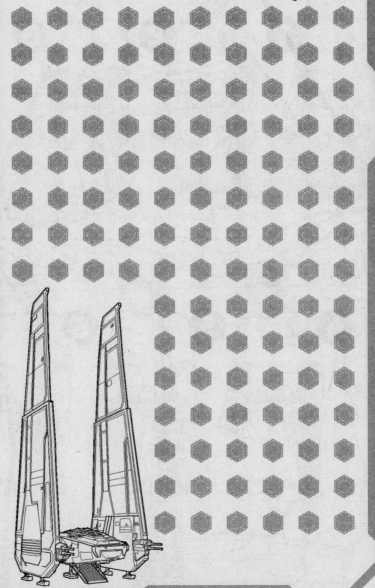

TROOPER TRAINING

The Stormtrooper uniform is known throughout the galaxy.
Can you spot the 2 troopers who are not the same?

Answer: 3 line on belt, and 5 line on leg.